DREAMS of C

❀ *Illustrations from C*

A BOOK OF POSTCARDS FROM THE LIBRARY OF CONGRESS

Pomegranate Artbooks/San Francisco

Pomegranate Artbooks
Box 808022
Petaluma, CA 94975

ISBN 1-56640-020-1
Pomegranate Catalog No. A606

Pomegranate also publishes several other postcard collections on different subjects.
Please write to the publisher for more information.

Cover design by Charlotte Kay Designs
Printed in Korea

The Library of Congress was established in 1800, when Congress appropriated funds for the purchase of 740 books and three maps. The new library was situated in "a suitable apartment" in the Capitol itself. When invading British troops burned down the Capitol in 1814, Thomas Jefferson offered to sell his wide-ranging personal collection of 6,487 volumes to Congress for a new beginning of its library. With those books came Jefferson's point of view that "there is, in fact, no subject to which a member of Congress may not have occasion to refer."

Under that broad allowance, the Library of Congress has ranged so widely across disciplines, nations and materials that it is now the largest library in the world, housed in three buildings near the Capitol. The illustrations collected for this book of postcards from a variety of children's books, magazines and stories reveal the depth of material for just part of one of thousands of subject areas embodied by the Library. They are also brought together here for the sheer enjoyment of rediscovering the art that made its first impression on us as children, that brought to life the characters and sets of both classic and obscure childhood tales, and that still holds for us the magic and wonder of the power of imagination.

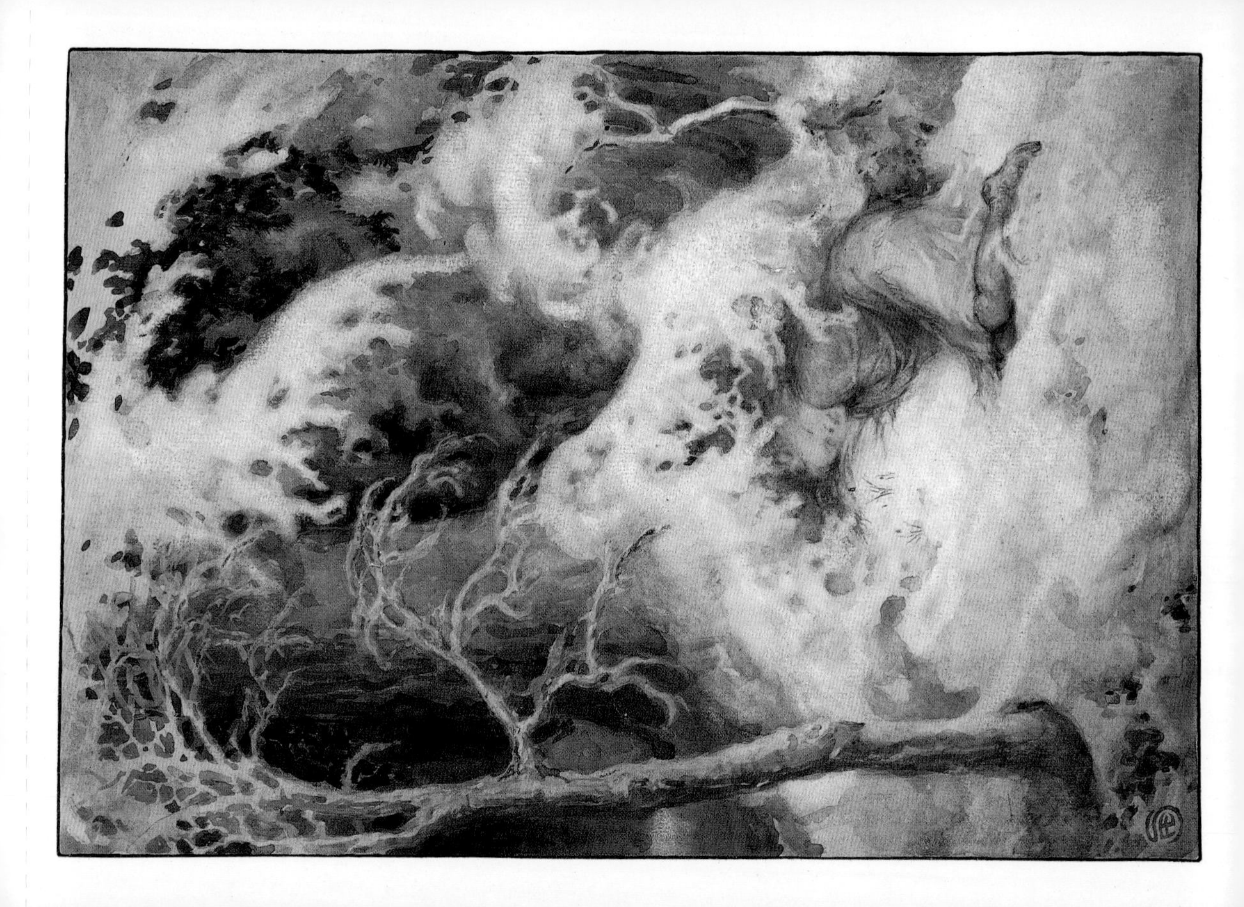

DREAMS of CHILDHOOD

Illustration by Florence E. Storer for "The Coming of The Prince" in *Christmas Tales and Christmas Verse*, 1912, by Eugene Field.

Then the pine-tree and the fir shook down the snow from their broad boughs, and the snow fell upon Barbara and covered her like a white mantle.

Pomegranate, Box 808022, Petaluma, CA 94975

DREAMS of CHILDHOOD

Illustration by Gertrude A. Kay from "Gold and Love for Dearie" in *Some Poems of Childhood*, by Eugene Field, selected by Bertha E. Mahony. Published by Charles Scribner's Sons, 1931.

Out on the mountain over the town,/All night long, all night long,/The trolls go up and the trolls go down,/Bearing their packs and singing a song . . . "Gold, gold! ever more gold— Bright red gold for dearie!"

Pomegranate, Box 808022, Petaluma, CA 94975

DREAMS of CHILDHOOD

Illustration from *"The Little Turtle That Could Not Stop Talking"* in *Folk Tales Children Love*, edited by Watty Piper. Published by Platt & Munk, 1934.

"Little Green Turtle is always talking," cried the children. "He can never keep from talking on a long journey."

That was more than Little Green Turtle could stand.

"I can, too," he cried. "I am not going to speak a word on the whole journey."

Pomegranate, Box 808022, Petaluma, CA 94975

DREAMS of CHILDHOOD

Illustration by Cecil Walton from *Fairy Tales*, by Hans Christian Andersen. Published by F. A. Stokes, c. 1911.

"She lighted another match, and at once she sat under the beautiful Christmas tree."

Pomegranate, Box 808022, Petaluma, CA 94975

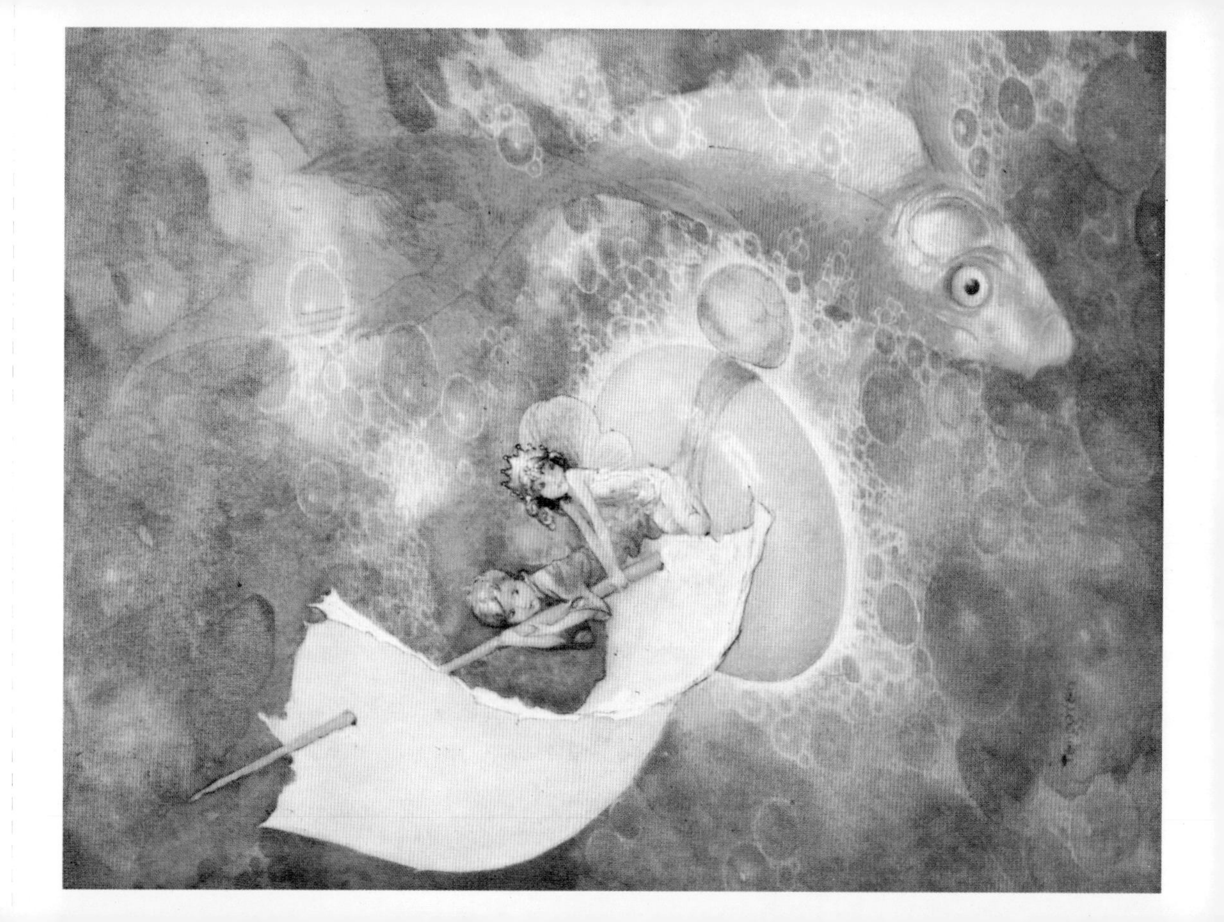

DREAMS of CHILDHOOD

Illustration by Gustaf Tenggren from *Dickey Byrd*, by Elizabeth Woodruff. Published by Milton Bradley Co., 1928.

Now, Dickey Byrd had often been inside that bathtub before, but he was astonished to see how big a bathtub can look when you're only the size of a safety-pin.

Pomegranate, Box 808022, Petaluma, CA 94975

DREAMS of CHILDHOOD

Illustration from *The Snow Queen*, by Hans Christian Andersen, illustrated by Katharine Beverley and Elizabeth Ellender. © 1929 by E. P. Dutton & Co., Inc., renewed 1957. Used by permission of Dutton Children's Books, a division of Penguin Books USA Inc.

"If I had not been a crow, I would have married her myself, notwithstanding that I am engaged."

Pomegranate, Box 808022, Petaluma, CA 94975

DREAMS of CHILDHOOD

Illustration by Edmund Dulac from "Bashtchelik (Or Real Steel)" in *Edmund Dulac's Fairy-Book*. Published by Hodder & Stoughton, 1916.

So the Prince set forth on his quest; and after three days' journey, he came to a beautiful city. And, as he rode beneath the walls of a castle, he heard a voice from a window, high in the tower, calling to him.

Pomegranate, Box 808022, Petaluma, CA 94975

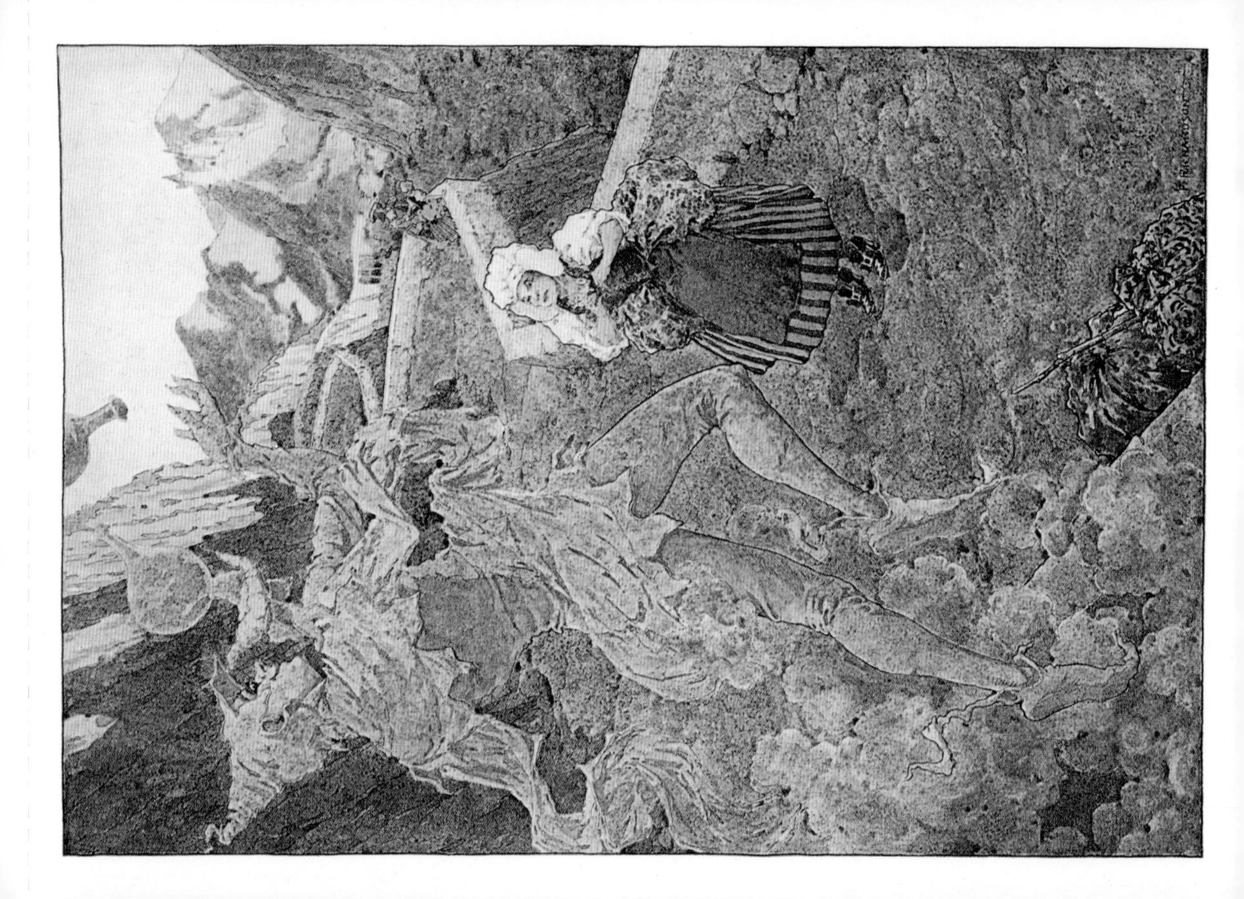

DREAMS of CHILDHOOD

Illustration by Frederick Richardson from *The Queen's Museum and Other Fanciful Tales*, by Frank R. Stockton. Published by Charles Scribner's Sons, 1906.

"Who on earth are you?"

Pomegranate, Box 808022, Petaluma, CA 94975

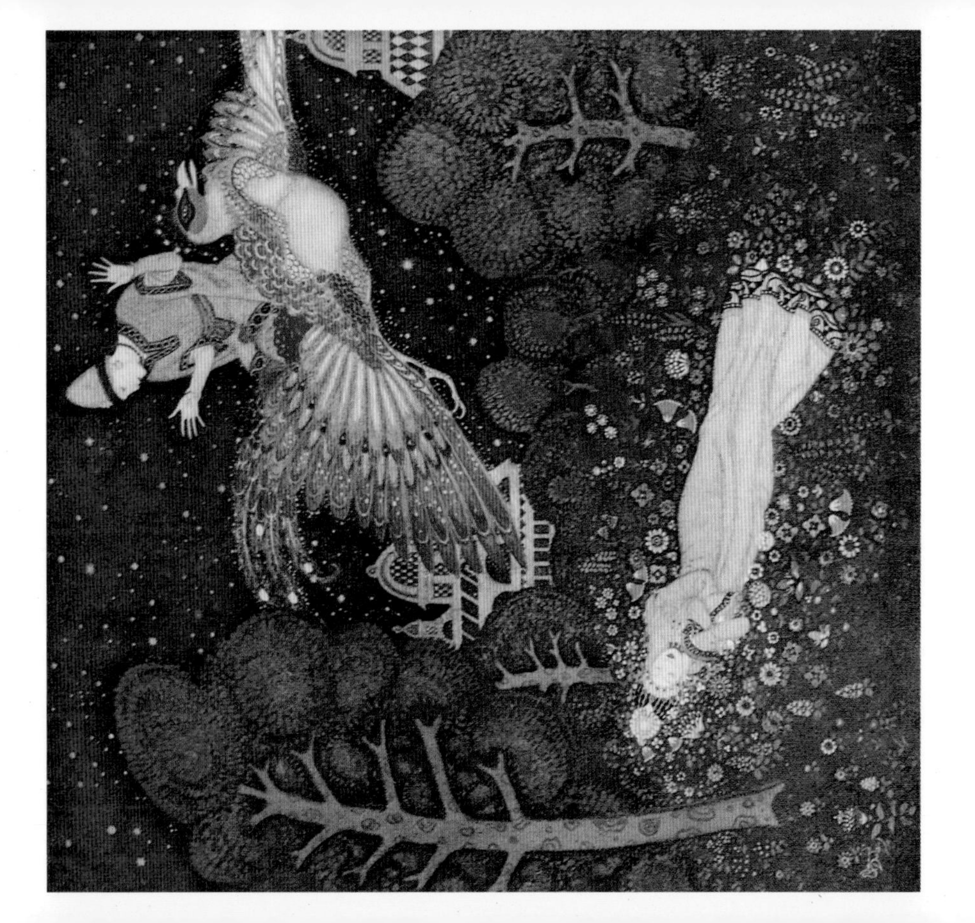

Dreams of Childhood

Illustration by Edmund Dulac from "The Firebird" in *Edmund Dulac's Fairy-Book*. Published by Hodder & Stoughton, 1916.

There is love, and there is love; but such love as sprang up at the same moment in two hearts can never be described. It was as if she had been dreaming about him all her life, and now she had awakened to find him. It was as if his journey had been to Paradise.

Pomegranate, Box 808022, Petaluma, CA 94975

DREAMS of CHILDHOOD

Illustration from "Why No One Ever Carries the Alligator Down to the Water" in *Little Black Stories*, by Blaise Cendrars, translated by Margery Bianco. Published by Payson & Clarke Ltd., 1929.

The alligator said: "I came to take a walk with my children, and all at once the water went down and it went a long, long way off behind us. Crick! Crack! I'm hungry!"

Pomegranate, Box 808022, Petaluma, CA 94975

DREAMS of CHILDHOOD

Illustration by Maxfield Parrish from *Poems of Childhood*, by Eugene Field. Published in 1904.

Pomegranate, Box 808022, Petaluma, CA 94975

Rare Book and Special Collections Division

3⟌912
746
x2

DREAMS of CHILDHOOD

Illustration from *Donald in Numberland*, by Jean Murdoch Peedie, illustrated by Berta and Elmer Hader. Published by Rae D. Henkle Co., 1927.

"But how is it I never heard you speak before?" he went on.

"Well," replied the 9, "you never stayed in school so late as this before. We never speak out loud during school hours."

Pomegranate, Box 808022, Petaluma, CA 94975

General Collections

DREAMS of CHILDHOOD

Illustration by Jessie Willcox Smith for *Waterbabies*, 1916.

"And there he saw the last of the gairfowl, standing up on the Allalonestone, all alone."

Pomegranate, Box 808022, Petaluma, CA 94975

KAY NIELSEN

DREAMS of CHILDHOOD

Illustration by Kay Nielsen from *East of the Sun and West of the Moon*, by Peter Asbjornsen. Published by Garden City Publ. Co., 1932.

So, when [the Prince] reached the spring, he too saw the image in the water; but he looked up at once, and became aware of the lovely Lassie *who sat there up in the tree. Then he coaxed her down and took her home; and at last made up his mind to have her for his queen.*

Pomegranate, Box 808022, Petaluma, CA 94975

LITTLE BOY BLUE,
COME BLOW YOUR HORN,
THE SHEEP'S IN THE MEADOW,
THE COW'S IN THE CORN.

DREAMS of CHILDHOOD

Illustration from *Mother Goose*, by Fern and Frank Peat.
Published by Saalfield Publishing Co., 1929.

Little Boy Blue,
Come blow your horn,
The sheep's in the meadow.
The cow's in the corn.

Pomegranate, Box 808022, Petaluma, CA 94975

DREAMS of CHILDHOOD

Illustration by Pierre Pinsard from "The Song of the Mice" in *Little Black Stories*, by Blaise Cendrars. Published by Payson & Clarke Ltd., 1929.

As he listened to their singing the husbandman began to dance. He danced, now sadly, now gaily, according to the words, the words of the mouse song.

Pomegranate, Box 808022, Petaluma, CA 94975

DREAMS of CHILDHOOD

Illustration by Maginel Wright Barney, frontispiece from *Lost Village*, by Alberta Bancroft. Published by George H. Doran Co., 1927, Doubleday Doran Co., donor.

Pomegranate, Box 808022, Petaluma, CA 94975

DREAMS of CHILDHOOD

Illustration by Feodor Rojankovsky from *Daniel Boone.*
Published by Domino Press, 1931.

"I would prefer more elbow room," Boone declared, as he placed his few possessions into a flat-bottomed boat—and, heading west, went down the Ohio and the Mississippi."

Pomegranate, Box 808022, Petaluma, CA 94975

JESSIE WILLCOX SMITH.

DREAMS of CHILDHOOD

Illustration by Jessie Willcox Smith, "Mrs. Doasyouwouldbedoneby," from *Waterbabies*, 1916.

Pomegranate, Box 808022, Petaluma, CA 94975

Cabinet of American Illustration, Prints and Photographs Division

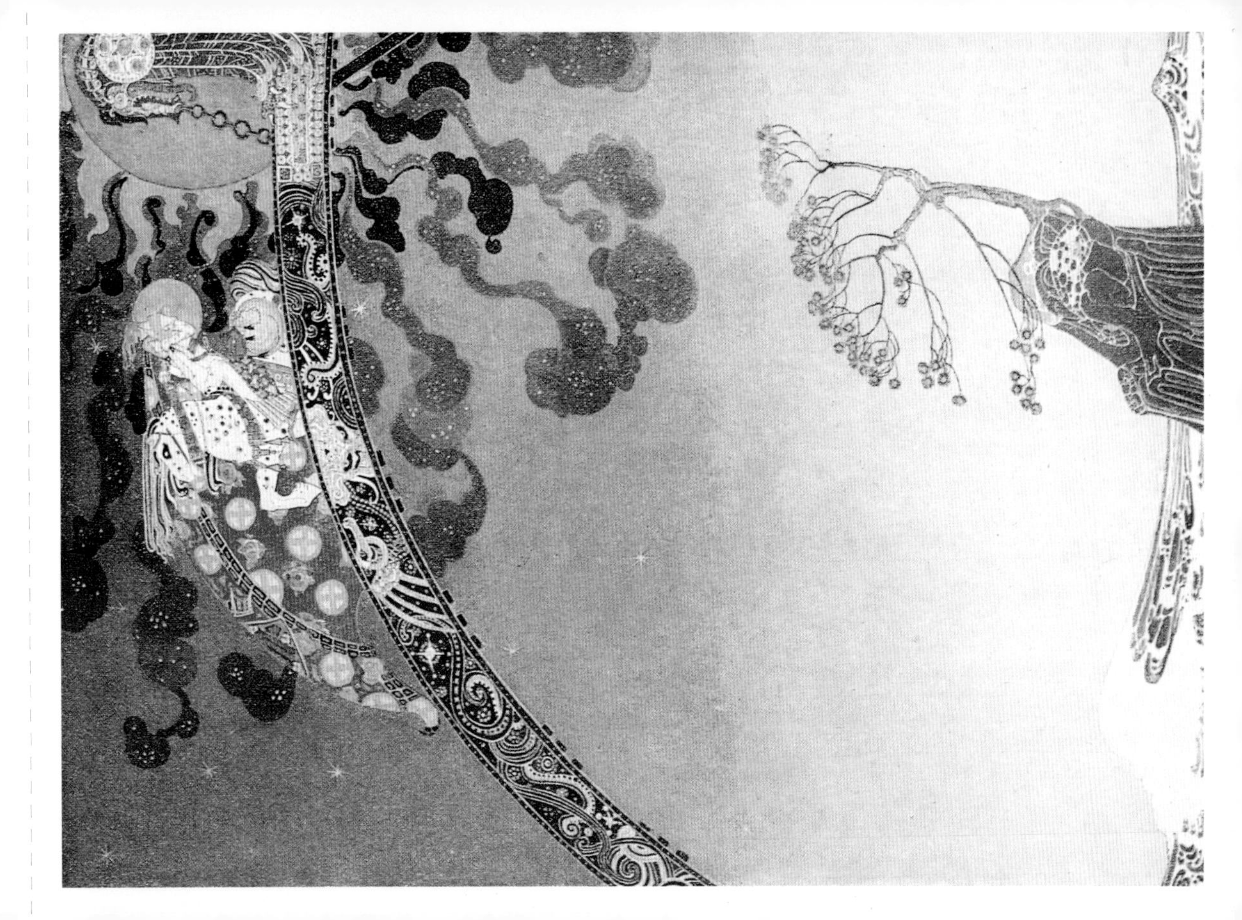

DREAMS of CHILDHOOD

Illustration by Kay Nielsen from *East of the Sun and West of the Moon*, by Peter Asbjornsen. Published by Garden City Publ. Co., 1932.

As for the Prince *and* Princess, *they set free all the poor Christian folk who had been carried off and shut up there; and they took with them all the silver and gold, and they flitted away as far as they could from the Castle that lay* East of the Sun and West of the Moon.

Pomegranate, Box 808022, Petaluma, CA 94975

PAINT BY MR AMOS
FERGUSON

DREAMS of CHILDHOOD

Illustration by Amos Ferguson for "Gazebo" in *Under the Sunday Tree*, by Eloise Greenfield and Amos Ferguson. Published by Harper & Row, Publishers, Inc., 1988.

As always/after he feeds the animals/the boy will go /into the gazebo/and stand looking out/at the landscape/marveling that his/eyes can travel/such a long distance/while his feet/stand still

Pomegranate, Box 808022, Petaluma, CA 94975

Dreams of Childhood

Illustration by Michel Sevier from *Children's Tales No. 6*, part of the series *Impressions of the Russian Ballet*, written and published by Cyril W. Beaumont, 1919.

The scene [from Massine's ballet Kikimora*] depicts the banks of the magic pool, lit by the pale-green rays of the moon. . . . Against this sombre background the Swan-princess dances sadly.*

Pomegranate, Box 808022, Petaluma, CA 94975

DREAMS of CHILDHOOD

Illustration by Edmund Dulac from "The Green Serpent" in *Edmund Dulac's Fairy-Book.* Published by Hodder & Stoughton, 1916.

Laideronnette kissed and embraced the good fairy Protectress.

Pomegranate, Box 808022, Petaluma, CA 94975

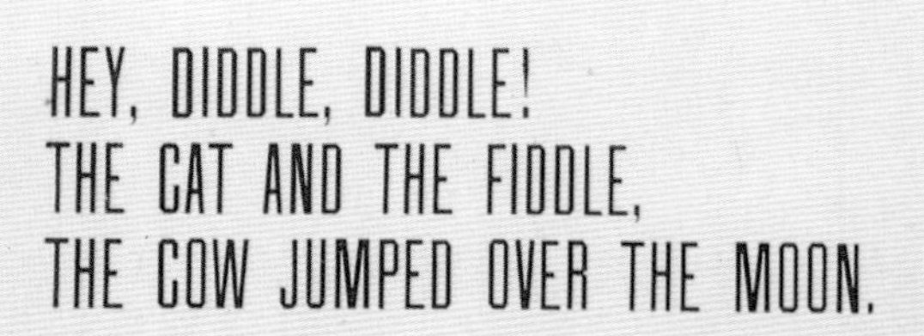

HEY, DIDDLE, DIDDLE!
THE CAT AND THE FIDDLE,
THE COW JUMPED OVER THE MOON.

DREAMS of CHILDHOOD

Illustration from *Mother Goose*, by Fern and Frank Peat.
Published by Saalfield Publishing Co., 1929.

Hey, Diddle, Diddle!/The cat and the fiddle,
The cow jumped over the moon;
The little dog laughed to see such sport;
And the dish ran away with the spoon.

Pomegranate, Box 808022, Petaluma, CA 94975

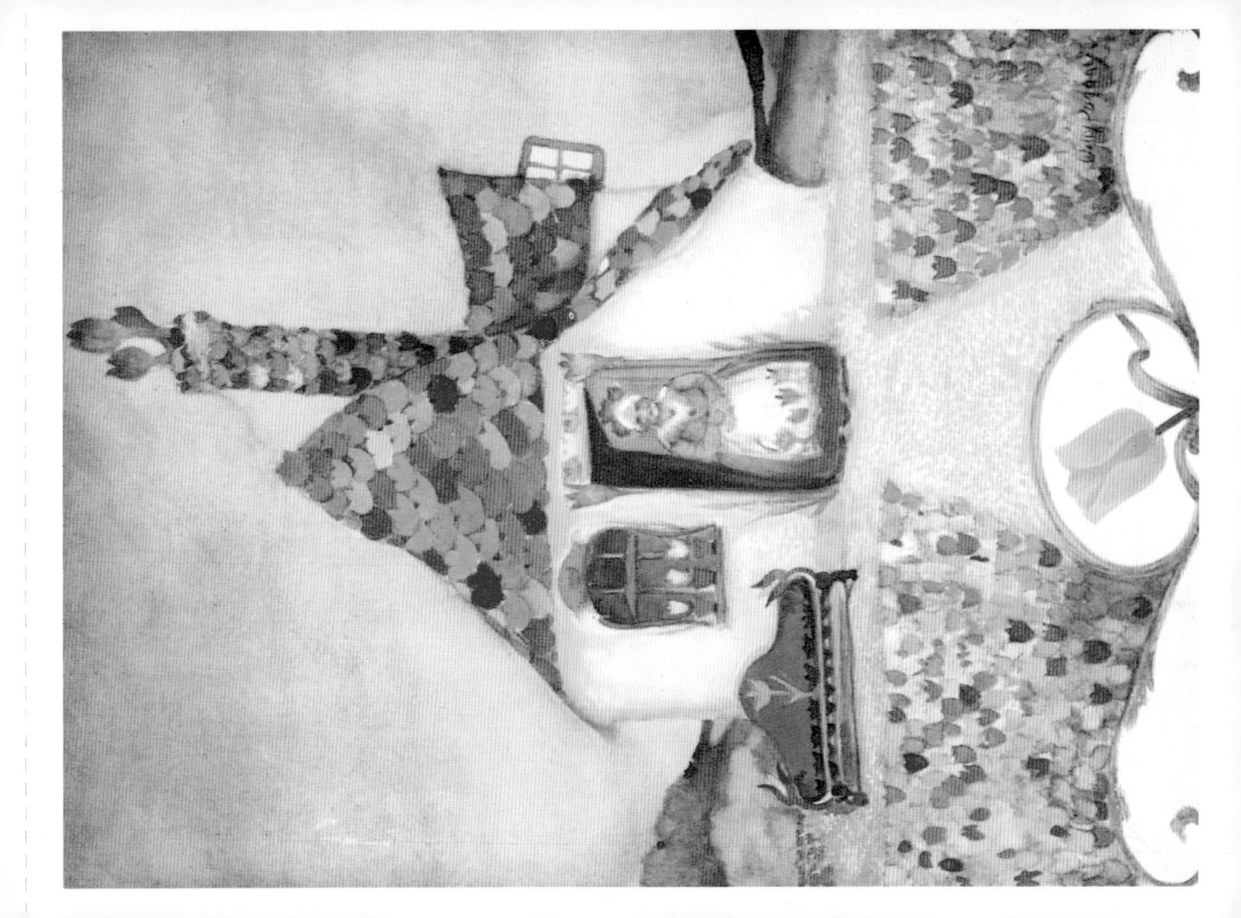

DREAMS of CHILDHOOD

Illustration by Willy Pogany from *Fairy Flowers*, by Isidora Newman. Published by Henry Holt & Co., 1926.

[Granny] planted hundreds of tulip cradles, which made the Pixies happy again. The tulips came up in hundreds, as beautiful as ever in colour, but they were very much smaller, as they are to this day.

Pomegranate, Box 808022, Petaluma, CA 94975

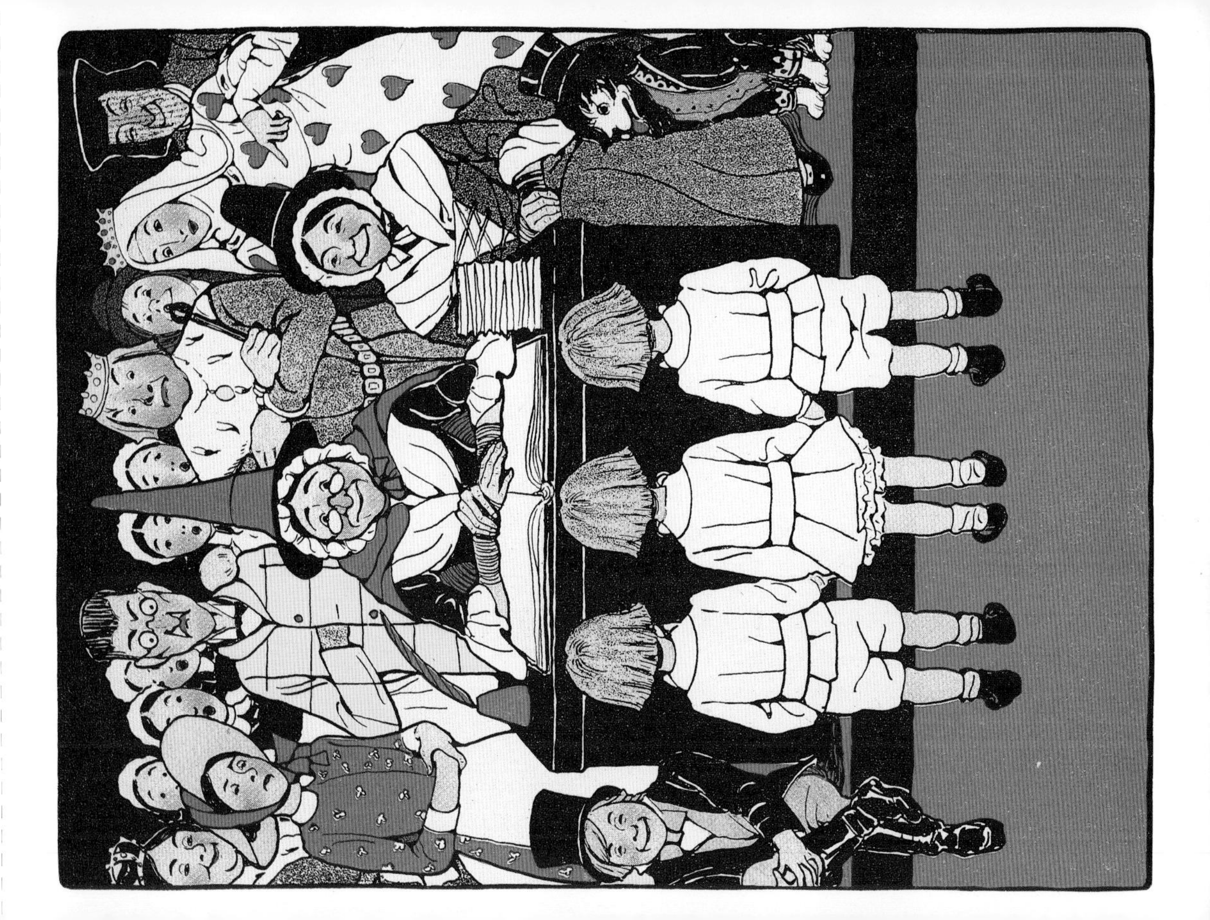

DREAMS of CHILDHOOD

Illustration from *The Land of Never Was*, by Millicent Olmsted, illustrated by Elenore Plaisted Abbott and Helen Alden Knipe. Published by George W. Jacobs & Co., 1908.

"State the offenses," said Mother Goose, who seemed to be the presiding officer.

Pomegranate, Box 808022, Petaluma, CA 94975

DREAMS of CHILDHOOD

Illustration by Michel Sevier, frontispiece from *Children's Tales*, part of the series *Impressions of the Russian Ballet*, written and published by Cyril W. Beaumont, 1919.

Pomegranate, Box 808022, Petaluma, CA 94975

Rare Book and Special Collections Division

DREAMS of CHILDHOOD

Illustration by Hawley Morgan from *The Adventures of Chippybobbie and His Friend Mr. Field Mouse*, by Mildred Batchelder. Published by Thomas Nelson & Sons, 1927.

Just at that very moment, Mr. Hippo did the thing he had been trying to do all the time. Mr. Hippo sneezed! . . . It was the biggest sneeze that was ever sneezed in all the world.

Pomegranate, Box 808022, Petaluma, CA 94975

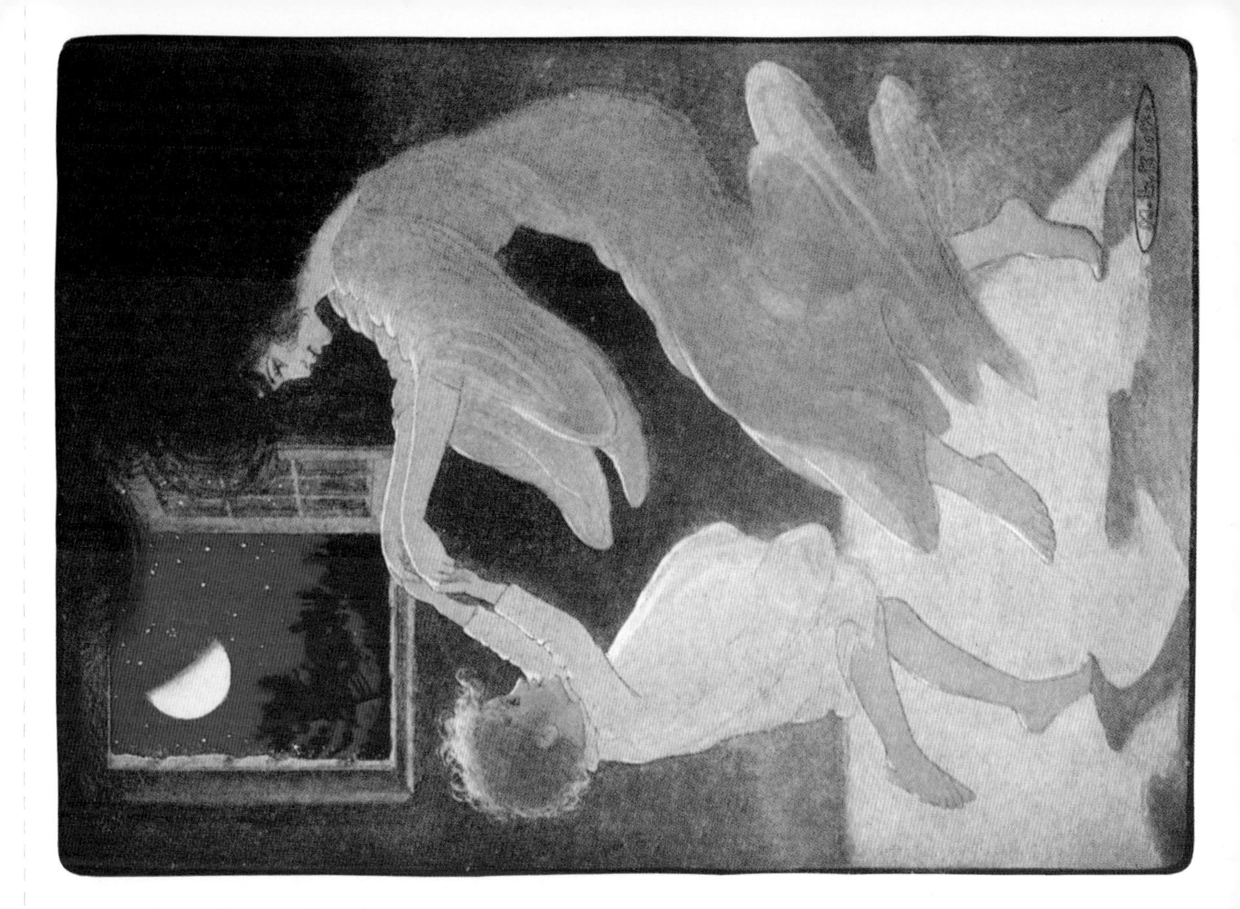

DREAMS of CHILDHOOD

Illustration by Maria L. Kirk from *At the Back of the North Wind*, by George Macdonald, simplified by Elizabeth Lewis. Published by J. B. Lippincott, 1914.

"Will you go with me now, little Diamond?" asked the North Wind bending over him and speaking very gently. . . . "People are not cold when they are with *the North Wind—only when they are against it. Now will you come?"*

Pomegranate, Box 808022, Petaluma, CA 94975

DREAMS of CHILDHOOD

Illustration by Edmund Dulac from "Ivan and the Chestnut Horse" in *Edmund Dulac's Fairy-Book.* Published by Hodder & Stoughton, 1916.

The chestnut horse seemed to linger in the air at the top of its leap while that kiss endured.

Pomegranate, Box 808022, Petaluma, CA 94975